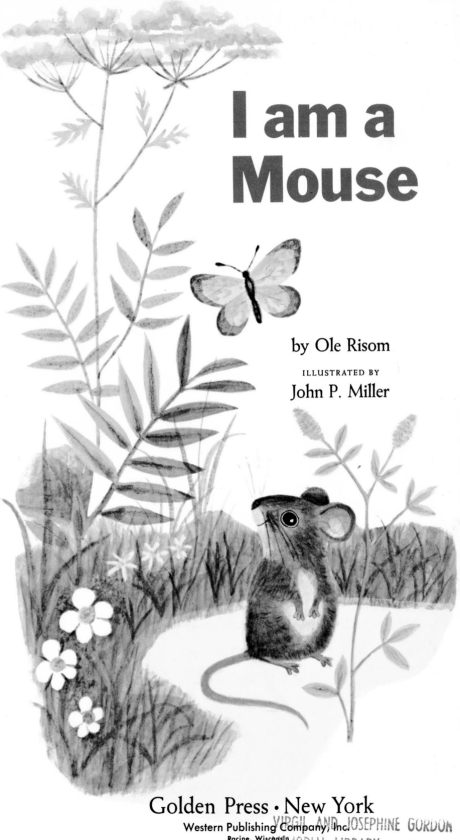

I am a Mouse

by Ole Risom

ILLUSTRATED BY
John P. Miller

Golden Press · New York

Western Publishing Company, Inc.
Racine, Wisconsin

Library of Congress Card Number: 64-9796   ISBN 0-307-62126-X

*M*y name is Deedee.

I'm quite small,

and I'm a mouse.

I live in the big field

near the woods.

Every day

I visit my friends.

This is my friend

the green katydid.

One of my neighbors

is the friendly green turtle.

He lives under the blackberry bush.

Sometimes I meet

my friend the snail

in the apple orchard.

There is a stream in our field.

I go there

to see the big trout.

9

Sometimes the ducks
come down to
the stream to swim.

Then we talk
together.

When I go in the woods

I always say hello

to my friends

the chickadee

and the woodpecker.

The shy newt

is hiding in the leaves

but he comes out

to say hello.

The chipmunks

are always cheerful.

They come running out

to greet me

whenever I come to call.

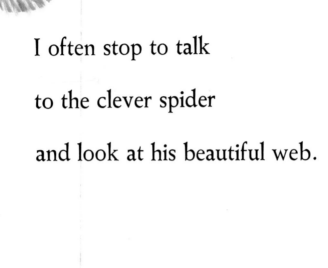

I often stop to talk

to the clever spider

and look at his beautiful web.

19

But when I see the owl

I hurry home

before he sees me.

Before I go

to bed at night

I watch the lovely

sun go down.